postman p

ANNUAL 1998

G000280157

Written by Brenda Apsley   Illustrated by Ray and Christine Mutimer
Designed by Jane Herridge   Cover design by Paul Dronsfield

Published in Great Britain in 1997 by World International Limited,
Deanway Technology Centre, Wilmslow Road, Handforth, Cheshire, SK9 3FB.

Printed in Italy.
ISBN 0 7498 3384 X

£5.50
UK only

Contents

A Message from Postman Pat

Hello! Welcome to my 1998 Annual. It's been a busy year in Greendale. You can read all about it in my annual. There are stories about spring cleaning, the summer fair, a windy day in autumn and some very odd things I collected for the Christmas jumble sale. You can also join Julian and me as we find out about nature through the seasons in Greendale, and learn about stamps and the post.

Rubbish!

It was spring in Greendale, and Sara had been busy spring cleaning the house. It was a good time to sort out any unwanted or broken things and get rid of them. She sorted out old pots and pans and plates from the kitchen. Then she helped Julian sort out his toys. He had outgrown some of them, but they wouldn't be thrown away. He packed them into boxes ready for the spring fair at school.

"Well done!" said Pat when he saw the boxes of unwanted things. "You've got rid of all the rubbish in the house."

"Not quite," said Sara. She took Pat outside into the garden and opened the door of the garden shed. It was full right up to the door. "There's lots of rubbish in here."

"But that's not rubbish," said Pat. "It's useful stuff. You never know when we might need it."

Sara held up an empty paint tin and a broken broom handle. "I don't think these will be useful for anything."

"OK," said Pat. "I'll sort it all out."

Pat spent a busy morning sorting out the shed. By lunch time he had lots of boxes ready for the next jumble sale. But there was still a pile of old stuff to get rid of. There was an old white sink, some snapped garden canes, bits of wood, bricks, metal hooks, Pat's old gardening clothes, old paintbrushes, a broken ladder and four big empty paint tins.

Pat likes to recycle things when he can, so he didn't want to take the rubbish to the tip. He thought hard. There must be a use for the things, if only he could think of it.

"Got it!" said Pat as he, Sara and Julian sat eating lunch.

"Got what, Dad?" asked Julian.

"A good use for all that old stuff in the shed," said Pat.

Pat got busy after lunch and after a couple of hours he loaded lots of things into the back of the van.

Julian went along for the ride. "I'll help you unload at the tip, Dad," he said.

But Pat didn't drive to the tip. His first call was to Black Beck Cottage. Pat had often helped Granny Dryden by holding up his hands so that she could wind knitting wool on them before rolling it into balls. Because she lived on her own she couldn't do it by herself, so Pat had made his 'Mark-One Wonder Wool Winder', which was really two half garden canes attached to a wooden base. Granny was delighted. "That's just the job!" she said.

Next stop was the post office. Mrs Goggins loves feeding the birds in the garden, so Pat had used bits of wood to make a little bird table for her. It even had hooks on the side so that she could hang up nets full of nuts in winter. "Another satisfied customer!" said Pat.

Pat's third stop was at Miss Hubbard's house. She's a keen cook and grows lots of herbs. Pat knew just what she would like. He put the old sink on brick 'legs' and filled it with soil so that Miss Hubbard could grow herbs right outside her kitchen door. Miss Hubbard couldn't wait to plant up her new herb garden.

Peter Fogg was pleased with the new scarecrow Pat had made for him. Pat propped it up on part of the broken ladder. The scarecrow had big paintbrush 'hands' and was dressed in Pat's old gardening clothes. "That will keep the birds off the seeds!" Peter called from his tractor. "Thanks, Pat."

There was one more thing left in the back of the van, but Pat took

that home with him. It was a new wooden scratching post for Jess.

Sara was pleased. "Now all you have to take to the tip are those four old paint tins and those bits of string," she said, looking in the neat and tidy shed.

"That's what you think," said Pat, and he disappeared behind the shed with Julian.

Sara got a surprise when they came back a few minutes later walking on paint tin and string 'stilts'! "A shed full of useless stuff?" laughed Pat. "Rubbish!"

Spring
in Greendale

Pat's favourite season is spring, when everything is new and green.

daffodil

tulip

snowdrop

cowslip

primrose

violet

Spring Flower Word Square

Pat told Julian the names of the spring flowers they saw on a walk. Can you find them in the word square? They are spelled out left to right, right to left, up and down. Tick each one as you find it.

p	r	i	m	r	o	s	e
i	e	n	a	k	i	p	h
l	i	d	o	f	f	a	d
s	n	o	w	d	r	o	p
w	d	m	o	c	l	f	s
o	b	v	i	o	l	e	t
c	j	p	i	l	u	t	j

The answers are on page 61.

Busy Birds

Spring is a busy time for birds. They find a place to build a nest and find a mate. Eggs are laid in the nest and have to be looked after until they crack open. Then comes the busiest time of all, with hungry young birds to feed.

Julian made a nesting scrapbook. He hung little bundles of wool, feathers, straw, twigs and string from a tree in the garden. He watched quietly and wrote down which birds came to collect the different things to make their nests. Why don't you do the same?

A bird book will help you name the birds. Here are some you might see.

blue tit

thrush

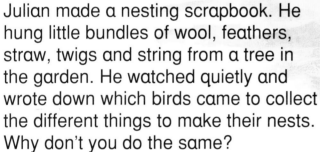

blackbird

chaffinch

Photographs by Kim Taylor, Michael McKavett and William S Paton, Bruce Coleman Limited.

Changes

Pat and Julian went for a nature walk one spring night. These two pictures look the same, but 5 things have changed in the second picture. Can you spot the differences?

The answers are on page 61.

Where in Greendale?

Postman Pat knows where everyone lives in Greendale. Do you? Can you match the villagers to their addresses?

1 Granny Dryden

2 Major Forbes

3 Alf Thompson

4 The Reverend Timms

5 Mrs Goggins

a Garner Hall

b Greendale Post Office

c Black Beck Cottage

d Thompson Ground

e The Vicarage

The answers are on page 61.

Make a Money Box

"I made a pillar box money box at school. Why don't you make one too? I'll show you how."

You will need:

a card tube from the middle of a toilet roll
card (cereal boxes are good for this)
non-toxic glue
Blu tac
red paint (or a red jumbo felt-tip pen)
black paint (or a black jumbo felt-tip pen)
a paintbrush

1 Paint or colour the card tube bright red. Leave to dry.

2 Cut out two circles of card. They should measure about 6cm across. Draw around an eggcup or a small top.

3 Paint or colour both sides of one circle black. Colour the other circle red. Leave to dry.

4 Put some glue around one end of the tube. Press it on to the black card circle. Leave to dry.

5 Ask a grown-up to help you cut a small piece of card from the other end of the tube. The cut should be about 3cm wide and 1cm deep.

6 Roll 3 tiny bits of Blu tac into little balls. Press them on to the open end of the tube.

7 Press the red card circle on top of the Blu tac to hold it in place.

"Now you can post your money into the pillar box money box. When you want to take money out, lift off the lid and press it back in place."

Four-legged Friends

1. One day the travelling fair comes to Pencaster. Pat and Sara take Julian after work. He wants to try all the rides.

2. Julian persuades Pat to go on the bucking bronco ride with him. The mechanical horse rears and bucks, tossing Pat into the air.

3. "Ride 'em, cowboy!" Julian calls. Pat lands with a thud on the saddle. His cap flies into the air. "Did you enjoy it?" asks Sara. Pat says nothing!

16

4. Next day Sara and Julian have a riding lesson. "Why don't you come too, Dad?" asks Julian. "OK," says Pat. "It can't be worse than the bucking bronco."

5. Sara and Julian have gentle horses to ride. Pat gasps when the groom hands his over. The horse is enormous, with big wild eyes.

6. "What's his name?" Pat asks. He looks alarmed when the groom tells him the horse is called Storm! "And he's quite a handful," she adds.

7. Sara and Julian set off. Pat tries to make Storm move off, but he ignores Pat. Pat is about to give up when Storm suddenly rushes off at speed.

8. Pat and Storm soon overtake Sara and Julian. "Whoa, boy!" shouts Pat, ducking to avoid a tree branch. He hangs on as Storm leaps over a hedge.

9. Pat is glad to be back at work next day. He is delivering the post when he sees a runaway horse and cart come rushing towards his van.

10. Pat steps into the horse's path and manages to hold its reins. He has to run hard to keep up with the horse, but at last he manages to stop it.

11. The owner is very grateful. "Thanks," he says. "You must have a way with horses." Pat shakes his head. "Oh, I wouldn't say that," he says.

12. That night Julian asks Pat if he wants to come to the horse show. "There'll be lots of horses to see." Pat shakes his head. "No. I've seen quite enough horses this week!"

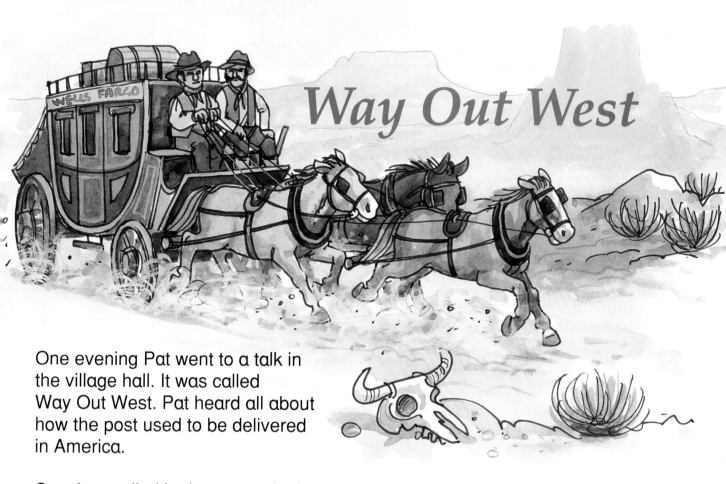

Way Out West

One evening Pat went to a talk in the village hall. It was called Way Out West. Pat heard all about how the post used to be delivered in America.

Coaches pulled by horses took six weeks to travel across the country. Then more than a hundred years ago, in 1860, horses and riders started to be used. Each rider rode a fast pony about 60km a day. They passed the post from rider to rider. This way the post took only eight days.

This postal service was called the Pony Express. Buffalo Bill was one of the riders.

Pat wondered what it was like to be a Pony Express rider. It sounded like very hard work. Pat decided he'd rather deliver the post in his van!

Coconuts!

One morning Charlie went into Trader's store. "Have you any spare coconut milk for my breakfast cereal?" Charlie asked. "I've run out."

Trader shook his head. "Sorry, Charlie," he said. "I'm out of coconut milk, too. And so is everyone else. You're the fifth person who's come in to ask for it this morning."

"Right, there's only one thing for it," said Charlie. "We'll have to harvest the coconuts." The coconuts usually fell from the palm trees by themselves, but for some reason this year they were late.

"If the coconuts won't come to us, we'll have to get them down ourselves. But how will we do it?"

Trader rushed off into the workshop at the back of his store muttering something about a New Improved Coconut Picker. He banged and hammered, busy on a new invention.

Idea!

Soon pebbles were falling all over the island of Merrytwit. They hit Charlie, Lewis, Arnold, and even Captain Mildred. But not one pebble hit a coconut.

Charlie went to ask Edward to help. "Look, you're a monkey," said Charlie. "You should be able to climb up the palm trees easily."

Arnold decided to use his weight. He ran against the tree trunks as hard as he could. He hoped to knock the coconuts down that way. One tiny coconut did fall down, and hit him right on top of the head. It wasn't ripe, and was very hard. Arnold rubbed the lump on his head and decided to give up on that idea.

Captain Mildred took charge as she always did. She asked the others to collect lots of pebbles and take them to her ship, the Buttercup. She explained why. "Because A, the pebbles will knock the coconuts down and B, we can fire them out of Buttercup's funnel."

Edward yawned and agreed to try. But he had only climbed a little way up the palm tree when he stopped and yawned a big yawn. His eyes started to close. "Sorry, Charlie, all this climbing has tired me out," he said, sliding down to the bottom of the palm tree again. "I need a nap." And before Charlie could answer, Edward was fast asleep.

21

When Mary the Hover Fairy arrived to find out what was going on Charlie thought his problems were over: Mary can hover as high as the tallest coconuts, and she said she would help. Mary flew to the top of the palm tree. But she was so tiny that she didn't have the strength to dislodge the heavy coconuts. She pushed and heaved, but not one coconut fell to the ground.

Charlie was staring up at the coconuts when Trader came out of his workshop at last. "What's that?" asked Charlie.

"It's my new invention," said Trader proudly. "My New Improved Coconut Picker with Maxi Power Trampoline."

Charlie shook his head. It looked more like some old elastic bands, a flour sack and a frame of bamboo held together with string.

"Now all we need is someone to bounce up on the Coconut Picker," said Trader.

He looked at Charlie. So did the others.

"You're not expecting ME to go up on this thing, are you?" said Charlie.

22

The others nodded. Yes, they were. "You're the obvious choice," said Trader. "You are an acrobat, after all."

Charlie couldn't argue with that. Shaking his head he walked across the clearing. He took a fast run up to the Coconut Picker. He leapt up on to the springy mat and bounced high, high into the air. He bounced down again, turned a double-double somersault, and soared into the air. He went up, up, even higher than the coconut trees, then came down again. His baggy pants filled with air like a parachute, and slowed him down. As Charlie passed the coconuts on his way down he grabbed one in each hand.

Charlie was kept busy for the rest of the day, bouncing up to collect the coconuts. Soon a huge pile sat outside Trader's store.

That evening Charlie was tired and a bit dizzy after all that bouncing about. But it was worth it. Now the islanders had enough coconuts to last them for ages. Trader gave Charlie a drink of coconut milk as a reward for all his hard work.

Everyone cheered and clapped. "Three cheers for good old Charlie!" said Captain Mildred.

"And three cheers for good old Trader!" said Lewis T Duck.

Charlie took a sip of coconut milk. "Cheers!" he said.

The Summer Fair

1. There is a big Summer Fair every year in Greendale. Everyone in the village works really hard to make it a big success.

2. This year the Summer Fair is held on a very hot day. The sky is clear blue with not a cloud to be seen. The sun shines from early morning.

3. Everyone helps to get things ready before the visitors arrive. There are lots of tents and stalls to put up on the village green.

4. Pat's special job is the Sweets-in-a-Jar Stall. People have to guess how many sweets are in a big jar. First, Pat has to count them all!

5. Pat starts counting. "68... 69... 70," he counts. Just then along comes the Reverend Timms. "Can you help set out some chairs, Pat?" he asks.

6. Pat helps with the chairs. But when he gets back to the sweet jar he can't remember how many he has counted. Is it 67? Or 76? Oh, dear!

7. Pat has to start counting all over again. "84... 85... 86," he counts, when Miss Hubbard rushes up. "Quickly, Pat," she says. "A leg has fallen off the cake stall!"

8. Pat is busy with a hammer and nails. When he gets back he can't remember how many sweets he has counted. Is it 68 or 86? He has to start counting again!

9. "99... 100... 101," Pat counts. Just then along comes Granny Dryden. "The roof has blown off my Fortune Telling tent," she says. "Can you help me fix it?"

10. The sun is shining and Pat is getting hotter and hotter. He starts counting the sweets again. "142... 143... 144," he counts. Then Ted Glen arrives.

11. "I've got to put up a big banner," says Ted. "Can you hold the ladder?" Pat puts the sweet jar on the table. He'll never get the sweets counted in time!

12. The summer fair is about to open as Pat wipes his head and counts, "247... 248... 249." Then Sara arrives. "Pat, can you help me?" she asks.

13. Pat ignores her! "250... 251... 252!" he counts, popping the last sweet into the jar. This time he writes the number on a piece of paper. "Now, can I help?" he asks Sara.

14. "It's my Wet Sponge Stall," says Sara. "I need someone to sit on a bench and have wet sponges thrown at them. I can't find anyone who will do it!"

15. Pat is hot and bothered. He wipes his head with a hankie. "Are they COLD wet sponges?" he asks, putting down the sweet jar. Sara nods. "Very cold."

16. Pat asks Julian to take over his Sweets-in-a-Jar Stall. Having cold wet sponges thrown at him is just what he needs after such a troublesome morning!

Summer
in Greendale

It's summer in Greendale. The sun is shining and the sky is blue.

Butterflies

Pat, Sara and Julian went for a walk in the meadow. There were butterflies everywhere. Pat told Julian all about them.

There are about 15,000 different kinds of butterflies. Most are brightly coloured. Their life cycle is in four stages. They look very different at each stage.

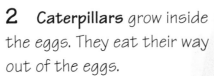

1 A butterfly lays lots of tiny **eggs**.

2 **Caterpillars** grow inside the eggs. They eat their way out of the eggs.

3 The caterpillar spends all its time eating. Then it changes into a **pupa**.

4 Inside its skin the pupa changes again. It comes out as a **butterfly**.

Here are some butterflies you might see in summer.

large white

small tortoiseshell

red admiral

28

Rainbows

There was a sudden rain shower when Pat, Sara and Julian were on their walk. The sun was still shining brightly. "Look," said Julian, "a rainbow!" Sara told Julian about rainbows.

When the sun shines on raindrops the sunlight splits up into a band of colours. This is a rainbow. You will see them on sunny days when it rains. Look **towards** the rain with the sun **behind** you.

There are seven colours in a rainbow.

red
orange
yellow
green
blue
indigo
violet

Poppies

The summer meadow is full of bright red poppies. How many can you count?

The answer is on page 61.

29

The Story of The Post

The postal service is a very useful one. We use it to send letters, cards and parcels. The postman or woman delivers them to the homes of our friends and family, often far away.

Millions of letters go through the postal system every day. Even those posted from the other side of the world arrive in a few days. How is this done?

The post works because of a network of sorting offices. Every letter is sorted many times before it arrives. Here's what happened when Julian's friend Michael sent him a birthday card.

Michael lives many miles from Greendale. He writes Julian's name, address and post code on the envelope. He sticks a stamp on to the top right-hand corner. Then he pops the card into the postbox. Post office workers collect the post from the postbox. They put it into sacks.

The post is taken to a sorting office, where all the letters are sorted. Those going to the same part of the country are put into the same sack. Machines make sorting easier. They can 'read' addresses and post codes. Some machines can sort 35,000 letters every hour!

Some letters and packages still need to be sorted by hand.

Now the post has to be taken to different parts of the country. Sacks are loaded on to vans, trains and aeroplanes. This often happens at night.

When the post arrives at the sorting office workers empty out the sacks. The letters are sorted again. Julian's card is taken to Pencaster. It then goes to a local sorting office. Next, Julian's card arrives at Greendale Post Office. Now the letters are sorted by street and road, then by house. Postmen and women deliver each letter. Where houses are close together they walk. Where houses are further apart they travel by bicycle or van, like Pat.

Before Julian is even awake his birthday card from Michael has been popped through the letterbox. Happy birthday, Julian!

Photographs © The Post Office 1997. Reproduced by permission of The Post Office.
The publishers would like to thank The Post Office for their help in the preparation of this feature.

31

Jess

A Day at the Seaside

It had been a hot, dry summer in Greendale. Pat had been working very hard.

On Friday morning there seemed to be even more post than usual.

"It's all these postcards," said Mrs Goggins as she handed sacks of post to Pat at the post office. "Lots of people are on holiday at the seaside."

Pat had a busy day delivering the mail. He couldn't help seeing all the postcard pictures showing sandy beaches and blue skies. He had lots of holiday brochures to deliver, too.

The brochures and postcards gave Pat an idea. "Shall we have a day at the seaside?" he asked Sara when he got home. "I need a rest. A deckchair on a quiet beach with the sun shining in a blue sky is just what I need."

Sara thought it was a good idea, and they set off bright and early next morning.

The sun was shining, the sea sparkled and the sand was warm under Pat's bare feet. Perfect!

Pat found a quiet spot on the beach. "I'm going to have a really good rest today," he said. "No rushing around, no beach cricket, just a lazy, quiet day."

Pat put up the big beach umbrella so that he could sit in the shade underneath it. But just as he got it up and sat down on his deckchair, a large beachball landed with a thud on top of the umbrella. Before Pat could move, the umbrella folded down again – with Pat underneath!

It took a few minutes before Sara and Julian were able to free Pat.

When Pat had put the umbrella up again he decided to cool down with an ice cream. Julian went to the ice cream van and came back with an extra large cone.

"Mmm, this looks good," said Pat. He was just about to take a lick when a cheeky seagull flapped along and tried to steal it.

"Waark!" said the seagull.

"Hey!" said Pat, throwing his arms up into the air.

The ice cream ended up in the sand!

This quiet day was not going quite how Pat had planned it.

Pat decided to read the newspaper. The sun was hot and soon he began to feel sleepy. He put his newspaper over his face and stretched out. He found a handy rock to rest his feet on. But someone else was already using the rock – a large crab! When the crab saw Pat's bare toe coming towards him he did what any crab would do – he pinched it. Hard!

"Ouch!" said Pat, leaping out of his deckchair. He bumped into the beach umbrella and it fell over into the sand.

Pat packed the umbrella away and went back to his deckchair. The gentle sound of the waves lapping against the sand was soothing. Pat relaxed, and soon he was asleep.

A few minutes later a big grey cloud blew in from the sea and soon large spots of rain started to fall. Pat woke with a start. Oh, no! Now it was raining. What next?

Julian had more bad news. "Look, Dad, the tide's coming in," he said. Soon the sea would cover the place where they were sitting. They would have to move – fast.

Pat and Sara had to hurry to pack everything away, and soon they were in the car on their way home again.

Pat was disappointed, but he was still determined to have a rest. "It's Sunday tomorrow," he said. "Another day off."

Sara looked alarmed. "We're not going back to seaside, are we?" she asked. "It wasn't much of a rest, was it?"

"No, we're not going to the seaside," said Pat. "I've got a much better idea."

But Sara and Julian had to wait until the next morning to find out what it was...

"Ah, this is the life. A peaceful day in Greendale-on-Sea!"

Test your Memory

Look carefully at this picture of Pat on the beach.
There are 8 things in the sand. Close the annual.
Can you remember all 8? Say the names out loud.

25 SUPER Postman Pat™ PRIZES

TO BE WON!

Would you like to own one of these great Postman Pat toys? You can, if you are one of the lucky winners in this year's Postman Pat Annual competition.

All you have to do to enter is to answer this question:

What are the names of Pat's wife and his son?

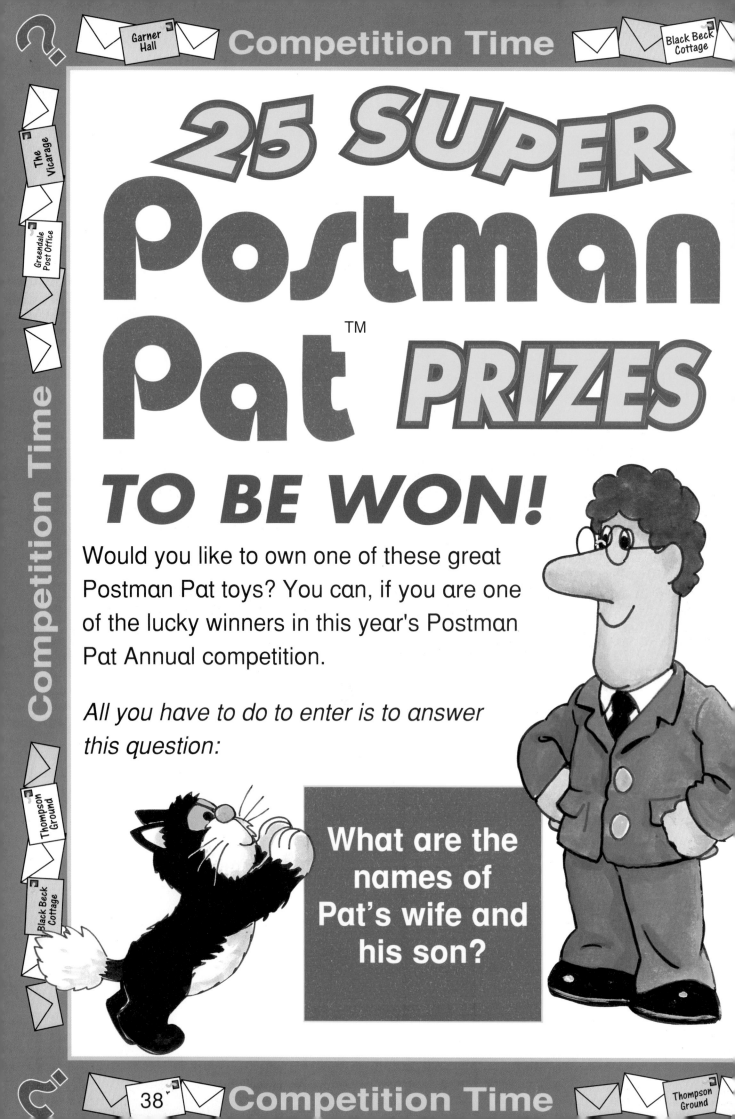

Garner Hall

Black Beck Cottage

The Vicarage

Greendale Post Office

Thompson Ground

Black Beck Cottage

Thompson Ground

You may be the lucky winner of one of these 25 top prizes, all made by Golden Bear:

10 large Postman Pat soft figures

10 huggable Jess soft figures

5 Postman Pat playsets,

which include a moving Pat doll, a postbox with opening doors and a slot for letters, and a post van with opening front and back doors.

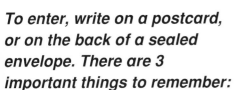

Photographs are courtesy of Golden Bear.

To enter, write on a postcard, or on the back of a sealed envelope. There are 3 important things to remember:

1. Write your answer to the question.
2. Tell us which prize you would prefer. Write Jess, or Pat, or Playset.
3. Don't forget to tell us your name, age and address.

answer................................
prize choice........................
my name...........................
age...........
address.............................
....
....

Send your entry to:

Postman Pat Annual Competition, World International Limited, Deanway Technology Centre, Wilmslow Road, Handforth, Cheshire SK9 3FB

The Apple Orchard Game

It's the end of summer and Pat and Julian are helping to pick apples in Major Forbes's orchard.

Play the Apple Orchard Game with a friend. One of you choose to be Pat, the other Julian.

You need 20 little buttons or counters each. You also need a coin.

40

To play, take turns to flip the coin. If the coin lands **HEAD** up, pick **I** of your apples by covering it with a counter or button.

If the coin lands **TAIL** up, pick **2** of your apples by covering them with counters or buttons.

The first player to pick (cover) all their apples wins the game.

You can play the game on your own, too. Every time you toss the coin, put a pencil mark on a piece of paper. Count how many turns it takes to cover the apples on BOTH trees. Can you cover them in fewer turns next time?

41

Trader's Portable Thingy

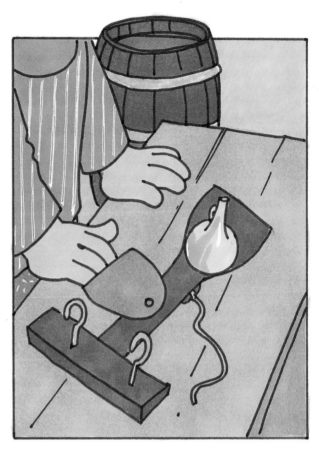

1. One fine, sunny morning on the island of Merrytwit Trader Jones is busy, working behind the counter of his store.

2. On the counter sits a very strange object. It looks like some sort of big handle. It has flat ends and bits and pieces stuck all over it.

3. Lewis T Duck comes in to buy some string. He looks around. "What's that?" he asks, pointing to the handle on the counter. "It's a portable," says Trader.

4. Edward comes to buy a frying pan. "What's that?" he asks. "It's a portable, of course," says Trader. "Oh," says Edward, puzzled. "Yes, of course it is."

5. Mary the Hover Fairy points her wand at the handle. "That's new," she says. "What is it?" Trader says, "It's a new portable." "Oh," says Mary.

6. Arnold comes in. "Do you have any new scarves in stock?" he asks. Trader goes into the back room to look. Arnold looks around the store.

7. Arnold notices the handle thing. "What's that?" he asks. "I've never seen one before." Trader looks over the pile of scarves he is carrying.

8. "Oh, that," says Trader. "It's a portable". "Ah," says Arnold, who has no idea what Trader is talking about. "I see, a portable. Very interesting."

9. Charlie comes in to see if Trader has a yellow button for his shirt. He has lost one. He looks this way and that at the handle. "What is it?" he asks.

10. Trader is fed up with answering the same question. "Isn't it obvious?" he asks Charlie. "It's a portable." Charlie shrugs. "Of course it is," he says.

11. When Captain Mildred comes into the store to buy a new mop she doesn't waste any time. "A, that's new," she says. "And B, what is it for?"

12. "It's a portable," says Trader. "A portable, eh?" says Captain Mildred. "But a portable WHAT exactly?" Trader shrugs. "I don't know," he says. "I haven't decided yet!"

Trader's Store

Charlie Chalk has given Trader a picture list of things he wants to buy from the store. Can you help Trader find them all? Tick each item as you find it.

Windy Weather

I. It is autumn in Greendale. The wind swirls dry brown leaves around. Pat is getting into his van to start his round when there is a big gust of wind.

2. The wind blows Pat's cap off his head. He chases after it up the street. Another gust of wind lifts the cap high into the air. It disappears over the church.

3. Pat will have to deliver the post without it. "Have you seen my cap?" he asks Granny Dryden. "No," she says, "but I found Major Forbes's deerstalker hat."

46

4. "I'll return it to him," says Pat. His next stop is at Thompson Ground. "The wind blew my cap away," Pat tells Alf Thompson. "Have you seen it?"

5. Alf shakes his head. "No, but this hat landed on my tractor just now." It belongs to Miss Hubbard. "Thanks, Alf," says Pat. "I'll take it back it to her."

6. Miss Hubbard is glad to get her hat back. Pat asks if she has seen his cap. "No," says Miss Hubbard. "But I found this cap stuck to my holly bush."

7. Pat recognises the cap. It belongs to Peter Fogg. "I'll return it to him when I go up to the farm later," says Pat. He gets back into the van and sets off again.

8. "Two letters for you, Major Forbes," says Pat. "And your deerstalker hat. Granny Dryden found it. I don't suppose you've seen my cap, have you?"

9. "No, sorry," says Major Forbes. "But my dog Snap found this hat when we were out walking this morning." It is Sam Waldron's. "I'll return it," says Pat.

10. Sam is outside his mobile shop. "Here's your hat," says Pat. "Have you seen my cap?" Sam takes a hat from his van. "No, but I found this one," he says.

11. The hat is Doctor Gilbertson's. Her house is next on Pat's round. She is pleased to have it back, but she hasn't seen Pat's cap on her rounds.

12. Pat looks everywhere for his cap, but there is no sign of it. He does find a hat stuck on the branch of a tree. But it isn't his. It's Ted Glen's.

13. "I've been looking for my hat all morning," says Ted. "You didn't see my cap while you were looking, did you?" asks Pat.

48

14. Ted hasn't seen Pat's hat, so he sets off to do his last delivery, at Peter Fogg's farm. Pat delivers Peter's cap as well as his envelopes and parcels.

15. Now Peter and everyone else in Greendale have their hats back, everyone except Pat. Where can his cap be? Pat heads back to the post office.

16. Pat is passing Peter's field when something catches his eye. Something small and blue. It's his cap – sitting on the head of Peter's scarecrow!

Autumn
in Greendale

Strong winds and colder weather mean that autumn has come to Greendale.

Leaves

Julian collected leaves that had fallen from the trees. He looked them up in a book at home to find out their names. Do you know them?

oak

beech

holly

horse chestnut

sycamore

ash

Julian made a leaf picture. He made an owl using brown leaves for feathers and two little yellow leaves for eyes. Leaf pictures are easy to make. Plan the picture first by moving leaves around on a sheet of paper. Then carefully stick them in place with little blobs of non-toxic glue.

50

Travelling Birds

Pat and Julian heard strange honking noises when they were out in the garden raking up autumn leaves. They looked up. The noises were made by lots of geese flying over.

"The geese are flying off to warmer places for the winter," said Pat. "They do it every year. They travel in large flocks (groups) because it's safer." The geese fly in a V shape. The goose at the front leads the way.

Pat and Julian see lots of swallows sitting on the telephone wires. They meet there before flying all the way to Africa. They fly here in spring because there is lots of food for them. When the weather gets colder here in autumn they fly back to Africa. These special journeys the birds make are called **migration**. Swallows fly more than 9,000km to Africa.

51

Stamp Spotting

Can you find 9 stamps hidden in this picture?

The Story of Stamps

Pat and Julian both enjoy collecting stamps. Julian finds out more about them in books from the library.

We put stamps on cards, letters and parcels to show that we have paid to have them delivered. Stamps have glue on the back. We lick them and stick them in the top right-hand corner of envelopes. When the post is sorted a machine makes a mark across the stamp to show that it has been used. This mark is called a postmark.

Post has been carried for hundreds of years. The first sticky postage stamps appeared in Britain more than 150 years ago, in 1840. It cost the same to post a letter however far it was to go – one old penny (much less than 1p today).

The first stamps were black, with a picture of the queen at that time on them. She was called Victoria. These stamps are called Penny Blacks, because they are black, and cost a penny! They are worth a lot of money today, because there are so few of them left.

Stamps are made in many colours and shapes. They all have different designs on them. Julian sticks his stamps into a special book called an album. He arranges the stamps by country. Some people collect stamps that have the same kind of picture on them, like birds or flowers, or this set of stamps showing toys and games.

Some stamps are so rare that collectors pay a lot of money to buy them. Some cost more than one million pounds!

A Very Berry Christmas

It was winter in Greendale. All the villagers were busy getting ready for the Christmas holiday and celebrations.

The Reverend Timms was collecting unwanted things for a jumble sale that was going to be held at the church. The money made at the jumble sale would help pay for the children's party after the carol singing. Pat offered to collect jumble when he went out delivering the post. There was plenty of room in the back of his van. "I'll get you some holly, too," said Pat. "I know you like to have lots in church."

"Thanks, Pat," said Reverend Timms.

Pat called at each house and farm where he had a delivery to make. Most people had sorted out unwanted things for the jumble sale. Pat thought some of them were very odd!

Major Forbes gave Pat an old tin hat, the kind soldiers wore to protect their heads many years ago. Who on earth is going to buy that old thing? Pat thought.

Miss Hubbard gave Pat some old books, a pair of very big leather gloves and some old goggles. She used to wear them when she rode a motorbike and sidecar when she was younger. Pat tried the gloves on – they reached right up to his elbows!

Granny Dryden gave Pat some plant seedlings in pots and some odd balls of knitting wool, all the colours of the rainbow. Oh, well, thought Pat. Someone might want to knit a stripy scarf with them.

Mrs Pottage gave Pat a plastic baby bath. "I used to bathe the twins in it," she told Pat. "But they're much too big for that now!"

At Thompson Ground, Alf and Bill gave Pat an even odder bit of jumble – one of their pigs' old, tin feeding troughs which had lots of little holes in the bottom. Pat laughed. "Now who do you think will want to buy that old thing, Alf?" he asked.

"You never know," said Alf. "Someone might find a use for it."

Pat shook his head. "I doubt it," he said, but he loaded it into the van with the rest of the jumble.

On the way back to the post office Pat spotted some holly bushes in the hedge at Peter Fogg's farm. Peter was in the field with his sheep, and told Pat he could take as much holly as he liked.

Pat started to collect the branches of holly. But it wasn't easy. The holly bushes were very tall and the bits with the best berries on were right at the top. Pat couldn't reach them. What could he do? Pat thought hard for a minute or two, then he snapped his fingers. "Of course!" he said, and opened up the back of the van.

He took out the old feeding trough. Standing on that, Pat could reach the best holly. But his problems weren't over. The holly bushes were very prickly. His cap got caught on a branch.

Pat needed something to protect himself. Then he remembered the tin hat. It was just the thing to protect his head!

Wearing the tin hat, Pat reached up for the holly. But the sharp, prickly leaves caught his hands. Those big leather gloves and the goggles that Miss Hubbard had given him were just what he needed.

Soon Pat had cut lots of holly. He used some of Granny Dryden's wool to tie it in bundles. He even found the perfect thing to carry it all in – the old plastic baby bath.

When Pat got to the church hall the Reverend Timms was delighted with the holly Pat had collected. He laughed when he saw the jumble Pat unloaded from his van, including the feeding trough, the leather gloves, the goggles, the baby bath and the old tin hat.

"I can't imagine anyone finding a use for those old things," said Reverend Timms. "Can you, Pat?"

Pat laughed. "You'd be surprised, Vicar!" he said. "Very surprised!"

Winter
in Greendale

Winter has come to Greendale.

Footprints in the Snow

Pat and Julian went sledging when snow covered the hills. On the way home Julian pointed to some footprints in the snow. "I wonder what made them?"

Pat pointed to Jess, who was walking ahead of them. The prints were made by his paws!

Can you match the footprints in the snow to the animals that made them?

1 duck   2 rabbit   3 horse   4 sparrow   5 fox

a   b   c   d   e

The answers are on page 61.

Stars

Dark winter nights are the best times for star watching. Pat and Julian wear warm clothes to look at stars. Join the dots from 1 to 7 to draw the star group called Orion.

Hibernation

Some animals sleep right through the cold winter months. They make warm nests, curl up and sleep right through until spring. Bats and hedgehogs do this.

This long sleep is called **hibernation**. In autumn squirrels hide food, such as acorns. They sleep in warm tree nests called **dreys** for much of the winter but wake up on warmer days to eat.

Photographs by Hans Reinhard and P Clement, Bruce Coleman Limited.

This squirrel has forgotten where it hid its acorns. Can you find 10 acorns?

hedgehog

grey squirrel

Julian has been looking at snowflakes. No two are exactly alike. Real snowflakes melt very quickly so Julian made some paper ones. Why not make some? They make good Christmas decorations.

1 Put a saucer or small plate on a piece of white paper. Draw around it. Use safety scissors to cut out the paper circle.

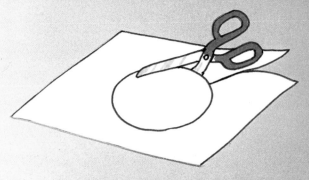

2 Fold the circle in half. Then fold it twice, like this.

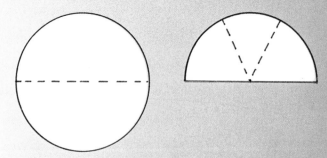

3 Use safety scissors to cut the top off the cone shape. Make little cuts on all three sides.

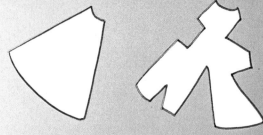

4 Open the folds to see your paper snowflake. Make lots. Like real snowflakes, no two will be just the same.

Answers to Puzzles

Page 10   **Spring Flower Word Square**

p	r	i	m	r	o	s	e
i	e	n	a	k	i	p	h
l	i	d	o	f	f	a	d
s	n	o	w	d	r	o	p
w	d	m	o	c	l	f	s
o	b	v	i	o	l	e	t
c	j	p	i	l	u	t	j

Page 12   **Changes**
1. Three bats are flying in the sky.
2. Pat's hat has changed colour.
3. The moon has disappeared.
4. The owl has moved.
5. Some eyes are watching them.

Page 13   **Where in Greendale?**
lc   2a   3d   4e   5b

Page 29   **Poppies**
There are 12 poppies.

Page 58   **Footprints in the Snow**
ld   2a   3c   4e   5b

61